CONTENTS

William Shakespeare:
The Man, the Actor, the Author

William Shakespeare is considered to be one of the greatest writers who ever lived.

He was born in the market town of Stratford-upon-Avon in Warwickshire, England in 1564 and died there in 1616.

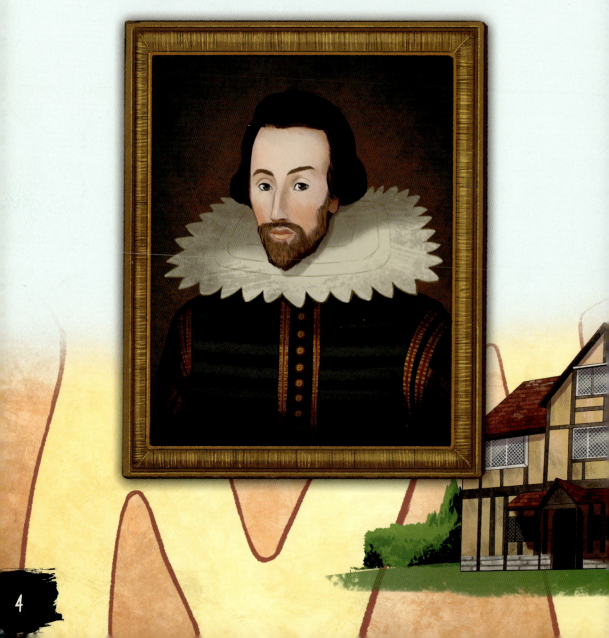

— SHAKESPEARE'S —

ROMEO AND JULIET

Adapted by
Steve Barlow and Steve Skidmore

Illustrated by Wendy Tan Shiau Wei

W

FRANKLIN WATTS

LONDON • SYDNEY

FRANKLIN WATTS
FIRST PUBLISHED IN GREAT BRITAIN IN 2022 BY HODDER AND
STOUGHTON

CREDITS:
EDITOR: GRACE GLENDINNING
DESIGNER: CATHRYN GILBERT
ILLUSTRATIONS: WENDY TAN SHIAU WEI

PICTURE CREDITS: PAGE 109 COLIN WATERS / ALAMY STOCK PHOTO
EVERY ATTEMPT HAS BEEN MADE TO CLEAR COPYRIGHT. SHOULD
THERE BE ANY
INADVERTENT OMISSION PLEASE APPLY TO THE PUBLISHER FOR
RECTIFICATION.

HB ISBN: 978 1 4451 8006 9
PB ISBN: 978 1 4451 8007 6

PRINTED IN CHINA

FRANKLIN WATTS
AN IMPRINT OF
HACHETTE CHILDREN'S GROUP
PART OF HODDER AND STOUGHTON
CARMELITE HOUSE
50 VICTORIA EMBANKMENT
LONDON EC4Y 0DZ

AN HACHETTE UK COMPANY
WWW.HACHETTE.CO.UK
WWW.HACHETTECHILDRENS.CO.UK

Shakespeare is usually referred to as an Elizabethan playwright but he actually lived during the reign of two monarchs: Elizabeth I and James I. When Elizabeth died in 1603, James, who was already King of Scotland, took over the English throne.

During Shakespeare's lifetime, he wrote nearly 40 plays and over 150 poems (mainly sonnets). He was also an actor, a very successful businessman and owned valuable buildings and land in London and Stratford.

His parents were John Shakespeare, a glove-maker and Stratford council official, and Mary Arden, who was the daughter of a wealthy local farmer. As the child of a reasonably well-off family, William attended the local grammar school, where he would have studied Latin and Greek as well as English literature and history.

In 1582, at the age of 18, he married Anne Hathaway. They had three children but by 1587, Shakespeare had left his wife and children in Stratford and moved to London. He joined an acting company and, by the early 1590s, was writing his own plays, becoming well known and successful in the world of London theatre.

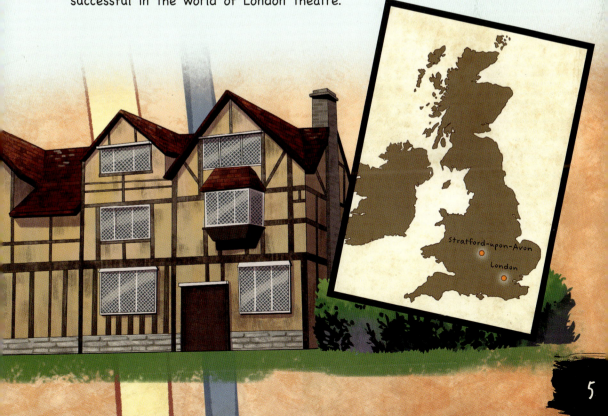

Stratford-upon-Avon

London

In 1594, Shakespeare joined a new acting company, The Lord Chamberlain's Men, with his friend, the actor Richard Burbage. He would spend the rest of his life writing plays to be performed by this company and even became a part-owner of The Globe Theatre, which was built in 1599. The Lord Chamberlain's Men were so successful that when King James came to the throne, he became their sponsor and their name was changed to The King's Men.

From 1610, Shakespeare began to spend more time in Stratford. He died on 23rd April 1616. In the years following Shakespeare's death, two of his friends, John Heminge and Henry Condell, collected manuscripts and copies of his plays. They were printed in 1623 in an edition known as *The First Folio*. This collection of tragedies, comedies and historical plays helped to establish Shakespeare as a great playwright – possibly the greatest the world has ever known.

Another friend, the playwright Ben Jonson, said that Shakespeare's plays would prove to be "not of an age, but for all time".

Jonson was right. Shakespeare's plays have been translated into every major language and are performed across the world. They have also been turned into films, TV series, musicals, ballets and graphic novels!

Romeo and Juliet – The Play

Shakespeare wrote plays of many different types. Among some of his greatest hits, *Hamlet* is a thriller, *A Midsummer Night's Dream* is a madcap comedy, *Macbeth* is a horror story, *The Tempest* is a fantasy, *Much Ado About Nothing* is a rom-com – and *Romeo and Juliet* is a love story.

Romeo and Juliet is one of Shakespeare's most famous and popular plays for good reason! It is fast-paced and action-packed with feuding families, fight scenes, young lovers, a secret marriage, dancing, music, jokes and a final death scene to make you cry ...

It is thought that Shakespeare wrote *Romeo and Juliet* between 1591 and 1595. It is considered to be the very first romantic tragedy to be performed on the English stage.

Since its first performance in Elizabethan London, *Romeo and Juliet* has been translated into dozens of languages and been performed across the world. There are more than 60 movie versions of it, and it has been the inspiration for over 30 operas, musicals and ballets. It is full of memorable characters and famous quotations ...

"What's in a name? That which we call a rose by any other name would smell as sweet."

Juliet Act 2 Scene 2

"But, soft! what light through yonder window breaks? It is the east, and Juliet is the sun."

Romeo Act 2 Scene 2

"Oh Romeo, Romeo, wherefore art though Romeo?"

Juliet Act 2 Scene 2

"Good night, good night! Parting is such sweet sorrow."

Juliet Act 2 Scene 2

"Oh, I am fortune's fool!"

Romeo Act 3 Scene 1

"Thus with a kiss I die."

Romeo Act 5 Scene 3

Although it was written over four hundred years ago, *Romeo and Juliet* continues to inspire and delight audiences. The play's themes are universal, dealing with family relationships, loyalty, hate, life and death; but first and foremost, it is a play about love ...

"For never was a story of more woe Than this of Juliet and her Romeo."

Prince Act 5 Scene 3

ROMEO AND JULIET

VERONA, ITALY
FIFTEENTH CENTURY

TWO RICH AND POWERFUL FAMILIES — THE MONTAGUES AND THE CAPULETS — HATE EACH OTHER.

BUT ROMEO MONTAGUE AND JULIET CAPULET MEET AND FALL IN LOVE ...

THEY DECIDE TO GET MARRIED WITHOUT TELLING THEIR FAMILIES.

WHAT COULD POSSIBLY GO WRONG ...?

List Of Main Characters
Dramatis Personae

THE MONTAGUES

ROMEO

Son of Lord and Lady Montague

LORD MONTAGUE

Head of the Montague family, enemy of the Capulets

LADY MONTAGUE

Wife of Lord Montague

BENVOLIO

Romeo's beloved cousin

THE CAPULETS

JULIET

Daughter of Lord and Lady Capulet

LORD CAPULET

Head of the Capulet family, enemy of the Montagues

LADY CAPULET

Wife of Lord Capulet

TYBALT

Juliet's beloved cousin

BALTHASAR

Romeo's servant

NURSE

Servant of the
Capulets and
Juliet's guardian

MERCUTIO

Friend of Romeo
and Benvolio,
related to
Prince Escalus

PRINCE ESCALUS

Ruler of Verona

COUNT PARIS

A nobleman who
is related to
Prince Escalus
and wants to
marry Juliet

**FATHER
LAWRENCE**

A Franciscan
monk

FATHER JOHN

A Franciscan monk
and friend of
Father Lawrence

APOTHECARY

A chemist living
in Mantua

THE PROLOGUE

VERONA, ITALY

These two rich and **powerful** families have **hated** each other for many years.

THE CAPULETS

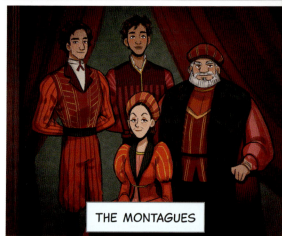

THE MONTAGUES

But such hatred only leads ...

... to **Death**.

And **so can love** ...

ACT 1

I **hate** the Montagues. I would fight them **all!**

Here's your chance. Insult them and let **them** start a fight.

Do you bite your thumb at **us**, sir?

No, sir! ... But I **do** bite my thumb!

13

BUT THEN ...

It's the Prince!

STOP FIGHTING, YOU ANIMALS!

Capulet! Montague! This is the **third** time your hate for each other has caused a **riot**.

If Verona's streets are disturbed again, those responsible will be **put to death**!

Montague, I will see you this afternoon.

Capulet, come with me!

Now, everyone GO!

Benvolio did you see **Romeo** in the fighting?

No, My Lady. Early this morning he was walking in the woods on his own.

He walks there **every morning**. Then he returns home and locks himself in his room.

We hear him **crying**. He won't tell us why he is **so sad**.

Here he comes. I will try and find out ...

Good morning, Cousin!

Still morning? When you are sad, time goes **so slowly**.

Why **are** you so sad?

19

THE INVITATIONS ARE SENT OUT.

My master has told me to invite the people on **this** list ...

... but I can't read!

If you find someone **else** to love, you'll forget about Rosaline!

Keep talking like that and I'll **break your leg**!

Good afternoon, Sire. Can you read?

Yes, if I know the language!

"The following are invited to a party: Martino, Count Anselme, Mercutio, Tybalt, Lucia ... **Rosaline**!"

Rosaline! Where is this party?

At my master's house.

And **who** is your master?

Lord Capulet. And if you're **not a Montague**, come along too.

You might meet one who is **more beautiful** than Rosaline!

Impossible!

Rosaline will be there!

And so will the **most beautiful women** in Verona!

I'm a **Montague**, but I'll go to **Capulet's** party because **Rosaline** will be there!

I know **exactly** how old. I've been her nurse for **all** of her life!

You were **such** a **pretty** baby. And one day you'll be a **beautiful** bride!

That is why I am here. The Count Paris wishes to **marry** you.

Oh he's a **wonderful** man! He'll be a **perfect** husband!

He is coming to the party **tonight**. Could you **love** him?

If you want me to, I will **try** ...

This will be a **happy** night!

25

Excuse me, but **who is** that lady?

I'm sorry, but I don't know.

I have **never seen true beauty** until now ...

Uncle, there is a **Montague** in **our** house! I will strike him **dead**!

It's only young Romeo. He isn't causing any trouble. **Leave him alone.**

But –

That is an **order**!

I **will** make the Montagues pay for this **insult**!

I hope you do not mind me taking your hand.

If you **do**, may I apologise with a **kiss**?

I am not upset at all.

Touching palms is how **saints** and **holy people** embrace.

Don't saints and holy people have **lips** too?

Then let us use our lips to pray ...

Of course! They use them to **pray**.

OUTSIDE THE
CAPULETS' MANSION

How can I leave my heart's desire? I **have** to see her again.

Romeo! Romeo!

He's gone home to bed!

He **jumped over** this orchard wall ...

I'll use a magic spell to bring him back! By the power of Rosaline's eyes, lips ... and **the rest of her** ...

... Appear!

He's **hiding.** Leave him be.

Let's go home ...

Goodnight, sweet Romeo!

31

34

Before I do, let us pledge our true love.

My love for you knows **no end**.

JULIET!

It's my **nurse**!

Just a minute!

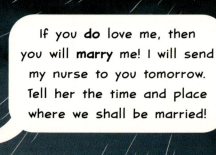

If you **do** love me, then you will **marry** me! I will send my nurse to you tomorrow. Tell her the time and place where we shall be married!

36

37

Father Lawrence!

Romeo! What brings you here so **early**?

You need to help me and my enemy ...

You talk in riddles!

I love Capulet's daughter, Juliet! **She** loves **me** and we wish to be married **today**!

I thought you loved **Rosaline**?

She never loved **me** ...

38

39

It's Romeo!

Where did **you** get to last night?

Oh, I had to deal with some important business.

What **sort** of "business"?

A gentleman would **never** tell ...

It was good though!

Well, it seems to have cheered you up!

We'll be at your father's for dinner, Romeo.

I'll follow you in a minute.

Farewell, old lady! **Old, old lady!**

SMACK

You let him **insult** me!

Juliet asked me to find you. I hope your thoughts towards her are honourable. She is young and should **not** be taken advantage of.

I **love** her!

Oh, that news will make her joyful!

I'll swap **my** bones for **your** news! **Tell** me!

Give me a moment to get my breath back ...

How can you be out of breath when you have breath to speak! **Tell me**, is your news good or bad?

About **Romeo**? I don't think you should choose him. He's handsome ... but not very polite ... Although ... I'm sure he is gentle ...

But do what you wish ... Have you had lunch yet?

47

May Heaven bless this marriage! I pray that nothing will happen to make us regret it.

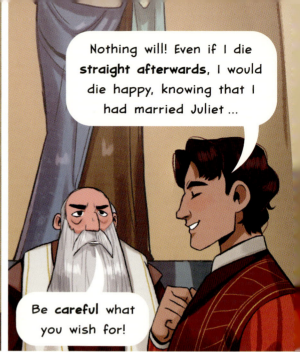

Nothing will! Even if I die **straight afterwards**, I would die happy, knowing that I had married Juliet ...

Be **careful** what you wish for!

Juliet! How **beautiful** she looks.

48

49

ACT 3

A SQUARE IN VERONA

Let's go home, Mercutio. It's too **hot**. On days like this, fights start for no reason.

Says the man who has a hot **temper**!

Hah! And what about **you?!** You're **always** looking to start a fight. I'm surprised you're not **dead!**

Oh **no!** The **Capulets** are here!

I don't care!

Mercutio, I want a **word** with you.

A word? How about a **fight** as well?

If you **want** one ...

51

53

CLANG

AARGHHH

Romeo, get away **now**! The soldiers are coming. If they capture you, you'll be sentenced to **death**! Hide in Father Lawrence's church.

Where is the man who killed the Prince's kinsman, Mercutio?

Tybalt, who lies there ...

You will come with **me** and explain everything to the Prince. **Now**!

57

I wish it was night and Romeo was here. I **can't wait** for us to be together.

What's the matter, Nurse?

He's **dead**! He's **killed**! Oh Romeo, why Romeo?

Is **Romeo** dead?

I saw his corpse with my **own** eyes.

No! It can't be! I will **kill myself** and join him!

Tybalt was my **friend** and now he's **dead**.

I don't understand. Are **both** Tybalt and Romeo dead?

59

What does the Prince say? Am I to die?

No, your life is spared. The sentence is **banishment** from Verona.

Banishment! That's **worse** than death!

Not if I have to leave Verona and Juliet! I'd rather be **dead**!

The Prince has been **merciful**!

KNOCK KNOCK

Listen to me! I can **help** ...

How? You're not young and in love like I am. You know **nothing**!

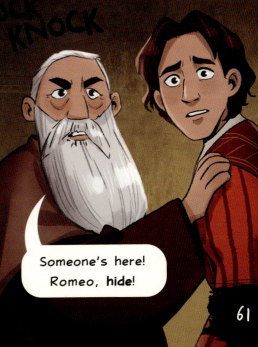

Someone's here! Romeo, **hide**!

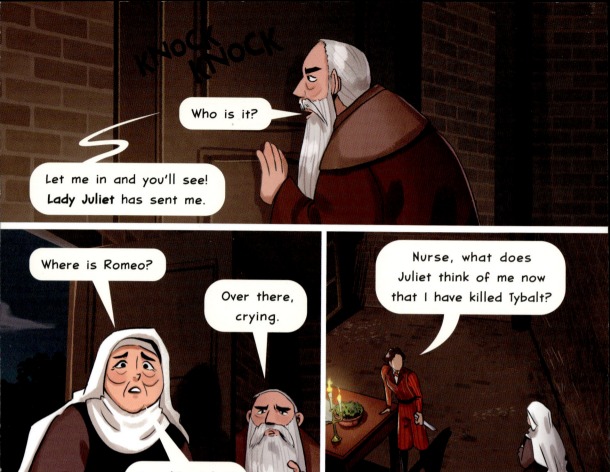

65

Mother, delay this marriage, **please** ...

Don't talk to me. Do what you want. I'm **finished** with you ...

How can this wedding be **stopped**? I'm **already** married to Romeo!

Romeo is banished forever. So, as things stand, I think you **should** marry Paris. He's better than Romeo in **every way**!

How **dare** you say that!

Thank you for your advice. Tell my mother I am going to Father Lawrence to ask for forgiveness for upsetting my father.

You **wicked** woman! I will **never** trust you with my secrets **again**.

FATHER LAWRENCE'S CHURCH

Thursday is very soon for a wedding!

Her father wants us to be married quickly. It will cheer Juliet up.

I'm sure it won't!

I'm happy to see you, my lovely wife ...

I'm not your wife ...

You will be on Thursday!

What will be, will be ...

Do you have time for my confession, Holy Father?

Yes, my child. Excuse us, Count Paris.

Of course. I will see you on Thursday, my dearest wife ...

71

You will be placed in the family vault.

I will write to Romeo and tell him to meet me in the vault. We will be there when you wake up.

Then Romeo can take you to Mantua and you will live together. Are you strong enough to do this?

Yes! Love will give me strength ...

Give it to me!

Juliet! Still asleep? **Wake up**, it's your wedding day!

No! No! Juliet is dead! My Lord! My Lady!

What is the **matter**? Bring Juliet downstairs. Count Paris is **waiting**.

He will wait **forever**. Juliet is **dead**!

She's dead!

Dead! I don't know what to say ...

76

Is Juliet ready to go to church?

She **is** ready to go, but will **never** return. **She is dead.**

My child! My **only reason** for living! **Dead!**

Juliet is married, but only to death. My hopes and dreams are **gone.**

What a **hateful, terrible** day!

My love in **life** is now my love in **death.**

Dry your tears! It is right to cry but be **happy** for her.

Juliet is in Heaven — a place of everlasting love.

The **wedding** will now be a **funeral.** Everything is the **opposite** of what it should have been.

Prepare for the funeral. We will follow Juliet to the grave ...

77

This is the shop that sells herbs and potions. I wonder if the chemist sells **poison** as well.

How can I help you?

You are poor. I'm sure **this** will persuade you to sell ...

I need a poison that will kill a man **instantly** ...

It's against the **law** to sell such a thing ...

Take this. It will do what you ask.

I will drink to Juliet and it will take me to her in Heaven!

79

Father Lawrence! Hello!

Father John, you're back from Mantua **already**? What did Romeo say?

Sadly, I didn't get to Manuta. On the way I visited a sick friend. The town officials thought we were **both** infected with the plague. They **locked us** in his house.

Who took my letter to Romeo?

No one – here it is ...

This is **bad** news! Juliet will be awake in **three hours** and locked in the tomb. I will have to go to her on my own.

Go and hide. If **anyone** comes, whistle.

These flowers are for my love. I will do this every night, forever!

Someone's coming. I need to hide, too ...

Leave me and take this letter to my father tomorrow morning. Farewell, my friend. And **thank you.**

I'm worried what Romeo will do. I'll stay and watch ...

85

Who's there?

Balthasar, Romeo's servant.

Where is Romeo?

He went inside the tomb half an hour ago.

This is not good ...

Whose **blood** is this? And whose **weapons**?

Romeo! He looks deathly pale. And **Paris**, covered with blood. What's **happened** here?

86

Juliet's waking up!

Father Lawrence! Where is my Romeo?

Our plan has gone **badly** wrong! Romeo lies **dead** on the floor, next to Paris. The Prince's men will be here soon. We **have** to get out of here!

Come with me ... I dare not stay any longer!

GO, **THEN**! I must **stay here** with my sweet Romeo ...

THE PRINCE'S PALACE

What is all this **noise?**

My Lord, Paris has been killed. Romeo is dead and Juliet, who was already dead, has been killed **again!**

We will go to the tomb, **immediately!**

THE CAPULETS' MANSION

Why are people **screaming?** Where are they going?

It **looks** like they are heading towards our family tomb!

We must follow them!

LATER, AT THE TOMB

My Lord, we caught these two.

No! Look how our daughter bleeds! Killed by **Montague's** dagger!

Oh, my daughter!

She came to me for help. She said she would kill herself if she had to marry Paris.

I gave her a potion that would make her **appear** dead.

Romeo was to **come back** for Juliet and take her to Mantua. I wrote a letter to him. But he never received it.

I went to the tomb and found Romeo dead. Juliet **refused** to leave with me. She **must** have used his dagger to end her own life.

Juliet's nurse knew about the marriage too. If you think I am to blame, then I should be punished.

95

THE END

Storytelling in *Romeo and Juliet*

The action of *Romeo and Juliet* takes place in less than five days.
The first two acts are based around the growing relationship of Romeo
and Juliet. After their wedding and the death of Mercutio and Tybalt,
the final three acts build towards the ultimate tragedy.

In the **PROLOGUE**, the themes of the play are introduced: love, honour, hatred and death. In
ACT 1, Shakespeare sets up the tension: Montagues and Capulets break out into a big fight.
In contrast to this violence, though, the act ends with Romeo and Juliet meeting at the
Capulets' house in a passionate (and famous!) moment of innocence.

In **ACT 2**, the play continues at pace. In the famous balcony scene,
Romeo and Juliet declare their love for each other and in a heartbeat,
decide to get married. Despite Father Lawrence's warning not to rush
into things, the two lovers get married in secret.

In **ACT 3**, the mood of the play turns from romance to tragedy. Mercutio and Tybalt
are killed; Romeo is banished. Romeo and Juliet get just one night together, and it's
the last time they will see each other alive. Romeo has to flee and Juliet has to marry
Paris. The destiny of the two lovers is determined and there's no going back.

ACT 4 is Juliet's act, and she is desperate. Father Lawrence's plan reflects
this: he doesn't know if it will work, but it is a risk Juliet is willing
to take, with terrible consequences. She is also deceitful towards her
parents, about marrying Paris and about her own death.

In **ACT 5**, the pieces are in place and the tragedy rushes towards its conclusion. Paris, Romeo
and Juliet will die and there is no avoiding this, in the tangled and violent web that's to be
woven. This is an act where things happen too late: the letter doesn't reach Romeo, Father
Lawrence doesn't get to the tomb in time and Juliet doesn't wake up before Romeo has killed
himself. If things had not been so rushed and hurried, the tragedy would have been avoided.

William Shakespeare – The Thief!

Like all writers, William Shakespeare was a magpie! Magpies like to take bits of other birds' nests to make their own. In the same way, writers can take ideas or themes from other writers and create their own stories. Shakespeare took stories from earlier times and other languages and adapted them for his audience.

The idea of a tragic love story is an ancient one! The Roman poet, Ovid, wrote a poem called *Metamorphoses* (meaning, Transformations) in the year 8 CE. In this poem he tells the story of Pyramus and Thisbe who are from feuding families. They fall in love, but Pyramus thinks Thisbe has been killed by a lion, so he kills himself. Thisbe isn't dead, but seeing Pyramus slain, she also kills herself (sound familiar?!). Shakespeare probably studied this story at school (he also retold it in another of his plays, *A Midsummer Night's Dream*).

However, there were more recent sources to "borrow" from as well ... In 1476, an Italian writer, Masuccio Salernitano, published a story called *Mariotto and Gianozza*. Many of the elements of the story we know today are present, although it is set in a different Italian city, Sienna.

This story was the inspiration for a novel, *Giulietta e Romeo*, written by Luigi da Porto in 1524 and published around 1530. da Porto changed the characters names to Romeo and Juliet and set the story in Verona. In fact, there were two Italian families living in the thirteenth century known for their feuding – the Montecchi were based in Verona and the Cappelletti in Cremona, a neighbouring city. These families owned two castles just outside Verona.

The Italian poet Dante mentions them in *The Divine Comedy*, an epic poem completed in 1320. (There is no evidence that there was a Romeo or Juliet in these families.)

In 1554, da Porto's novel was rewritten by Matteo Bandello and was then translated into French by Pierre Boaistuau in 1559.

This French version inspired *The Tragical History of Romeus and Juliet* by Arthur Brooke, a 3,020-line poem written in 1562.

This poem was then retold in prose by William Painter in 1567 in his book, *Palace of Pleasure*. And this is all still more than 25 years before Shakespeare put pen to paper for his version.

There is also some evidence that Shakespeare was aware of a real-life feud between two Elizabethan families. The Danvers and the Longs had an age-old feud that involved secret marriages, street brawls and murder! So ... Shakespeare took parts of an English translation of a French translation of an Italian translation, added some ancient texts and a little dash of modern reality, and created *Romeo and Juliet*!

Themes in Romeo and Juliet

Although *Romeo and Juliet* is a play that explores the theme of dangerous young love, there are many more themes in the play that contribute to it being so interesting to watch and study. Antithesis means the opposition of words or phrases against each other, such as hot and cold, fast and slow. *Romeo and Juliet* is a play full of opposites that have varying effects on one another.

Montague vs Capulet

The rival families' hatred is at the heart of the play. There were plenty of aristocratic families in England who hated each other when *Romeo and Juliet* was written, so this theme was a word of warning to its original audience as much as it is to today's readers! Instead of overcoming their differences for the sake of peace, Shakespeare's characters allow them to ruin their lives.

Love vs Hate

The love of Romeo and Juliet is contrasted with the hate of the families. The word love is said about 107 times in the play, but around it swirls violence and sorrow. The hate spoils the love, which can't survive within the rotten context of the families' hate.

Light vs Dark

Romeo and Juliet's relationship is described in terms of both light and darkness. It is the obvious passion contrasted with its ultimate doom. Romeo describes Juliet as being like "the sun".

"She burns more brightly than the torches at the party"

Act 1 Scene 5

Stars, lightning and burning fireworks are also images that are used to describe their love.

However, the images of darkness and hatred lurk around at all times. They have to meet in secret, at night and this is when they spend most of their time together until they die together in the darkness of the tomb (see page 90). In fact, at the end of the play, the Prince announces that even the sun will not shine on this gloomy morning. Darkness wins out.

Fate vs Choice

Who is responsible for what happens? Do events occur because of the way the characters act or is it because it is "written in the stars"? Humans have asked this question for millennia.

Romeo and Juliet are described as "star-crossed lovers" at the very beginning of the play. In other words, it seems they are helpless to change what is going to happen to them, as it has already been decided by fate. Even Romeo describes himself as being "fortune's fool" and takes no responsibility for what happens.

But Shakespeare's writing makes us consider this closely: does the tragedy happen because of ...

- The Capulets' and Montagues' history of feuding?
- Romeo and Juliet going against their parents' wishes?
- Father Lawrence trying to unite the families without asking?
- Tybalt's and Mercutio's hot-headed fighting?
- The Chemist for giving Romeo poison?

- The wedding of Paris and Juliet being brought forward a day?
- A letter not being delivered on time because of the plague?
- Juliet not waking up at just the right time?

Or are they all steps towards a pre-written fate? What do you think?

Stories such as *Romeo and Juliet* are timeless because they explore themes we can consider in our own lives and prompt questions we can ask about the world we live in.

Fast vs Slow

There are many images of time in the play. This helps to show the rushed nature of Romeo and Juliet's relationship and contrasts the recklessness of the young with the experience of the older characters. The lovers meet and within minutes decide to wed (see page 36)!

In contrast, Lord Capulet originally tells Paris he should wait for two years before marrying (although he does change his mind). Father Lawrence, too, tells Romeo to slow down in his haste to get married. He warns,

"They stumble that run fast." **Act 2 Scene 3**

Shakespeare's Language

Inventions

Shakespeare used more than 20,000 different words in his plays and poems. Around 1,700 of these were new or were the first recorded use of the word! He invented new words and phrases by making them up or by putting two words together to make a new one, or adding or subtracting parts of words.

The (at the time) entirely new phrase, "wild-goose chase" in Romeo and Juliet is just one example of Shakespeare's brilliance with language.

Puns and Word Play

Shakespeare uses a lot of word play throughout his plays and Romeo and Juliet is no exception. There are over 170 puns in the play!

As Mercutio is dying he says:

"Ask for me tomorrow and you shall find me a grave man."

Act 3 Scene 1

What he really means is not that he's going to be serious tomorrow ("grave") but that he's going to be IN a grave (i.e. dead!).

Shakespeare's audience would have loved this type of joke – there are a lot of rude ones as well, too cheeky for these pages!

Poetry

Shakespeare's works were often written in a mixture of verse and prose (normal speech). Important and high-ranking characters (kings, lords, etc.) usually speak in verse. Prose is more likely to be spoken by servants.

Romeo and Juliet contains both verse and prose, but mainly a form of verse called "blank verse". Nearly 87 per cent of the play is poetry and the remaining 13 per cent is prose.

Blank Verse

This is a type of poetry that follows these rules:

- Each line has 10 or 11 syllables.
- Each line has five strong beats.

Think of a heart beating: de **DUM** de **DUM** de **DUM** de **DUM** de **DUM**. This is similar to how the beat or stress falls on the syllables in the verse. See how this works in Romeo's last line (all the words are one syllable long).

When you say the line, you would place the emphasis on the word in bold.

De - **DUM** - de - **DUM** - de - **DUM** - de - **DUM** - de - **DUM**

Thy - **drugs** - are - **quick.** - Thus - **with** - a - **kiss** - I - **die.**

Sonnets

In contrast to blank verse, a sonnet is poem that has 14 lines and a strict rhyming pattern. When Romeo and Juliet first meet and talk, it sounds like "normal speech" but is actually a sonnet!

A Soliloquy

This is a speech spoken by one character; we're listening to their thoughts. They are thinking out loud to themselves, or speaking directly to the audience, not to another character. (In the graphic novel, we have put some of these in "thought bubbles".)

Juliet's 'Balcony Scene' speech is a soliloquy (see page 33). We are listening to her true thoughts about Romeo. She doesn't know that Romeo is listening.

Fun Facts

Juliet is really a man!

In Shakespeare's day only males could act on the stage. All the female parts were actually played by males! To make it all even more complicated, several of Shakespeare's plays, including *Twelfth Night*, *As You Like It* and *The Merchant of Venice*, have female characters pretending to be male. So, when you watched one of these plays you were watching a man pretending to be a woman pretending to be a man!

Coming next!

Romeo and Juliet begins with a prologue where we are told what is going to happen during the play.

"A pair of star-crossed lovers take their lives."

But when *Romeo and Juliet* was published in the First Folio in 1623, there was no prologue! It was in the quarto that had been published in 1597, but in the first folio edition the prologue disappeared! We still don't know if the cut was deliberate or a mistake. (See page 106 for more info on folios and quartos.)

Where are you? WHY are you?

Probably the most famous line in the play is said by Juliet in the balcony scene.

"Oh Romeo, Romeo, wherefore art thou Romeo?"

But Juliet isn't wondering where Romeo is (he's actually below her!). To Shakespeare, "wherefore" was a common word that meant "why". So, Juliet is actually saying, "Why are you called Romeo?" (She's sad that he's one of the Montagues – the hated enemies of her family, the Capulets).

Line up!

* There are 3,093 lines of text in *Romeo and Juliet*.

* 2,610 lines of poetry (about 87% of the play)

* 393 lines of prose (about 13% of the play)

* Lines spoken by male characters – 2,086 (about 69%)

* Lines spoken by female characters – 935 (about 31%)

* But Romeo and Juliet speak nearly an equal number of lines.

Publication

Shakespeare's plays weren't printed or even written up as complete plays before they were first performed. Each actor was given his part on a scroll. They had to learn their lines from this.

The "platt" or plot of the play was a list of the scenes with the exits and entrances. This was posted backstage for the actors to follow.

Shakespeare's *Romeo and Juliet* first appeared in print in a book called the *First Quarto* in 1597, although two more versions (the Second Quarto and Third Quarto) were published in Shakespeare's lifetime in 1599 and 1609.

It was also published as part of the *First Folio* in 1623, when 36 of Shakespeare's plays were published together for the first time.

Book Fact

There were three main sizes of books in Shakespeare's time.

Folio

A book made from sheets of paper that are folded once to make four pages from one sheet.

Quarto

A smaller book. The sheets of paper are folded twice to make eight pages from one sheet.

Octavo

An even smaller book! The sheets of paper are folded four times to make 16 pages from one sheet.

Performing The Play!

In Shakespeare's time, drama performance and theatre spaces were developing in various ways across the globe. England was no exception.

When Shakespeare began his acting career, there were very few theatres in London.

Plays were performed in inn yards and in the halls and houses of the monarch or the wealthy. But, by the end of Shakespeare's life, plays were being performed in purpose-built theatres across London, where performances took place every day (except Sundays), all year round.

The first purpose-built London playhouse appeared in 1576 when James Burbage, father of Shakespeare's friend, Richard Burbage, constructed a building for performing plays. He called it The Theatre! The success of this space led to other playhouses being built across London.

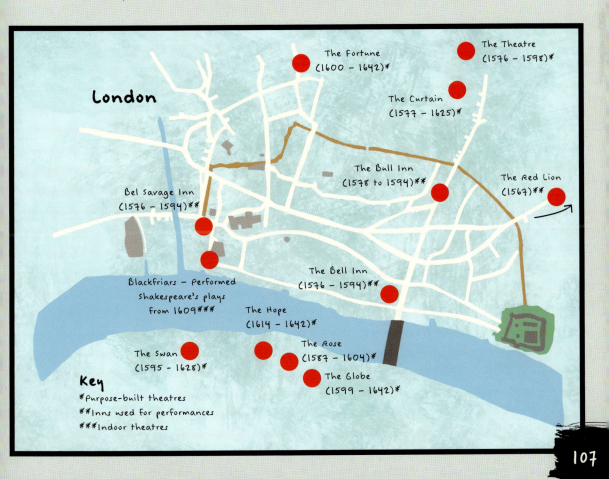

London

The Fortune
(1600 – 1642)*

The Theatre
(1576 – 1598)*

The Curtain
(1577 – 1625)*

The Bull Inn
(1578 to 1594)**

The Red Lion
(1567)**

Bel Savage Inn
(1576 – 1594)**

Blackfriars – Performed
Shakespeare's plays
from 1609***

The Bell Inn
(1576 – 1594)**

The Hope
(1614 – 1642)*

The Swan
(1595 – 1628)*

The Rose
(1587 – 1604)*

The Globe
(1599 – 1642)*

Key
*Purpose-built theatres
**Inns used for performances
***Indoor theatres

Deadly Serious Fact

"A plague on both your houses!"

Bubonic plague, or the Black Death, was a big part of Shakespeare's world. Thousands of people died from the plague across the globe.

It is thought to have been passed on by rat fleas, which carried deadly bacteria. If you caught the plague, there was a fifty-fifty chance of survival. Whenever there was an outbreak in London, the theatres were shut down, which meant no money for playwrights or actors.

The Theatre

A trip to the theatre to see a play in Shakespeare's time was very different from today. People didn't sit still. They stood, walked around, shouted and chatted to each other. The audience could buy ale, wine, pies, fruit, tobacco and nuts, all while the play was being performed. The audience got as close to the action as possible, so they could hear the actors – there were no microphones in Shakespeare's day!

The plays were aimed at all levels of society – from Lords and Ladies of the court down to tradespeople and commoners. Criminals also visited the playhouses, ready to pick the pockets of unsuspecting members of the audience.

Depending on how rich (and important) you were, you could choose where to sit.

In 1594, a worker's pay was about 8 pence a day, so it meant that plays were affordable to a lot of London's population and therefore many people went to the theatre. The large theatres, such as The Globe, could hold up to 3,000 spectators, including 1,000 groundlings (see opposite).

For indoor playhouses, it was more expensive and therefore the audience members were wealthier.

The Globe Theatre was built in 1599.

The Globe Theatre

There would be a different show every afternoon. Coloured flags advertised what play was being put on that day.

Open-air playhouse

Thatched roof

Galleries

Red – History

Black – Tragedy

White – Comedy

Stage

(Under stage and above stage used for special effects, storing costumes and changing rooms for actors)

Standing area (groundlings)

GLOBE ADMISSION COSTS

1 Penny
Be a groundling. Stand in the yard around the stage.

2 Pence
Sit on a wooden seat in one of the three tiers (galleries).

3 Pence
Have a wooden seat and hire a cushion to keep your bottom a little more comfortable!

6 Pence
Sit in the Lord's Gallery to Rooms on either side of the balcony at the back of the stage.

12 Pence
(1 shilling)
Sit on the stage.

30 Pence
(2 shillings & 6 pence – or half a crown)
you could sit in a private box.

Glossary

The World of Shakespeare's Words

Early Modern English Language was only about 100 years old when Shakespeare started writing in the sixteenth century. Because he often wrote in verse, in order to fit the words into the necessary rhythm, some of the sentence order seems odd to us today.

As Shakespeare was writing over 400 years ago, some of the words and phrases he uses can look a bit strange. Some are so old, that we don't use them any more!

Thou, thee, thy and thine

Shakespeare uses these words A LOT. But they aren't as confusing as they seem!

thou	means	you
thee	means	you
thy	means	your
thine	means	your

Sometimes two words are put together. Watch out for the apostrophe!

'twas	means	it was
'twere	means	it were
'tis	means	it is
is't	means	is it

Sometimes words have extra letters. Take off the **t** or **st** and see what's left!

hast	means	has
wilt	means	will
dost	means	does
thinkst	means	think
hath	means	has
didst	means	did

Some more old words:

art	means	are
ere	means	before
forfeit	means	penalty
forsaken	means	abandoned
hence	means	from here
hie	means	go (hurry)
wherefore	means	why
ye	means	you
yonder	means	there
fie!	means	an exclamation of disapproval

Shakespeare Timeline

We often have no clear information about the dates of Shakespeare's plays. Scholars who study Shakespeare have to rely on information such as the way each play is put together, the language Shakespeare uses and details in the text that connect to parts of history.

Therefore, the dates of the plays given below are 'best guesses' as to the years in which they were written and first performed.

1558 Queen Mary I dies and her sister, Queen Elizabeth I, takes the throne of England.

1564 Shakespeare is born. Horse-drawn coaches first appear in England.

1567 The first purpose-built theatre in England is built – The Red Lion in Stepney, London.

1576 The Theatre is built in London by James Burbage. 180,000 people now live in London. 300,000 live in Paris, France.

1582 Shakespeare marries Anne Hathaway.

1582 The theatres close down in London due to an outbreak of plague. Thousands of people die.

London's first waterworks is founded.

1583 Susanna (Shakespeare's daughter) is born. (See also 1585)

1584 Ivan The Terrible, first ruler of Russia, dies.

1585 Hamnet and Judith (twins – Shakespeare's son and daughter) are born.

1587 Shakespeare leaves Stratford-upon-Avon and his family for London.

The Rose Theatre is built in London by Philip Henslowe (on Bankside).

Mary Queen of Scots is executed.

1588 The Spanish Armada invade England, but are defeated.

1590/1 Shakespeare's first plays, **THE TWO GENTLEMAN OF VERONA** and **THE TAMING OF THE SHREW**, are performed.

1591 Shakespeare dedicates his poem, *Venus and Adonis*, to the Earl of Southampton. This poem earns him a lot of money!

Tea is first drunk in England.

1592 Shakespeare is mentioned in the press as an up-and-coming playwright.

Plague! All London playhouses are closed for two years.

Many of the acting companies tour the country.

Shakespeare begins writing poems.

The Imjin Wars between Japan and Korea begin.

1593 Playwright and friend of Shakespeare, Christopher Marlowe, is killed in a brawl.

1594 Shakespeare's poem, *The Rape of Lucrece*, is published. Again, it is dedicated to the Earl of Southampton.

1595 Shakespeare becomes a shareholder in The Lord Chamberlain's Men (a very successful and popular acting company).

ROMEO AND JULIET

1596 Shakespeare's son, Hamnet, dies. Shakespeare's father, John, is granted a coat of arms.

England sees its first tomatoes – and its first flushing toilet.

A MIDSUMMER NIGHT'S DREAM

1597 Shakespeare buys New Place in Stratford – one of the largest houses in the town.

Transportation to English colonies is first used as a punishment for criminals.

1598 **MUCH ADO ABOUT NOTHING**

1599 The Globe Theatre is built.

1601 **HAMLET**

Shakespeare's father dies.

1603 Queen Elizabeth dies.

James VI of Scotland takes the throne with the title James I.

Plague hits London. Over 30,000 people die. The theatres are closed again.

The Lord Chamberlain's Men change their name to The King's Men.

They perform at the King's courts and are recognised as the leading theatre company of the time.

1604 The Globe reopens.

1605 The Gunpowder Plot fails to blow up King James and his ministers.

In Spain, Cervantes publishes Part 1 of the world's first novel, *Don Quixote*.

1606 **MACBETH**

Theatres are ordered to close if the weekly number of people who die from the plague rises above 30.
Theatres closed July – December.

1607 Shakespeare's daughter Susanna marries John Hall, a physician in Stratford.

Shakespeare's brother, Edmund (an actor), dies.

Founding of Jamestown, Virginia – first English colony in North America.

1608 Shakespeare's mother, Mary, dies.

Shakespeare becomes a grandfather! Elizabeth is born to Susanna and John Hall.

The King's Men begin to perform at an indoor theatre at Blackfriars.

The telescope is invented by a Dutch scientist and used by Galileo.

1609 Shakespeare's *Sonnets* are published.

The Blue Mosque is built in Constantinople.

1610 Shakespeare spends more time in Stratford.

1611 **THE TEMPEST**

1612 Shakespeare's brother, Gilbert, dies.

The decimal point is first used by German mathematician Pitiscus.

The Dutch establish a trading post on Manhattan Island (later New York).

1613 The Globe Theatre burns down during a performance of Henry VIII.

Shakespeare buys a house in Blackfriars, London.

1614 The Globe Theatre is rebuilt.

1616 Shakespeare's daughter, Judith, marries Thomas Quiney, a Stratford wine merchant.

Shakespeare dies.

1623 Shakespeare's plays are published. the *First Folio* contains 36 of his plays.